GRAY JOLLIFFE
Christmas already!

Written and Illustrated by Gray Jolliffe

An Essex House Publication

Bit of a tricky one, this! We want a Jewish gag book about Christmas — mildly offensive but not over the top — light but uncompromising — no filth — make it risky but don't overdo it. Get the picture?

OK, pregnant is only a few lousy months
— but this I have to wear all my *life*??

Uh Oh, it's at Bernie's place! That's a bad start!

Ask yourself Mr. Claus — how can I justify a further facility to someone who appears so consistently in the red?

Different lipstick? New gown? I give up — what's different?

It's Christmas, I'm pregnant, God knows how — and now you tell me
you forgot to book a room! Terrific!

Leonard, would you do me a favour?..
Anything!
..As we're such old friends?..
Any thin
..As its Christmas nearly?...
Anything!
..And as I don't have a penny to my name?..
Almost anything!

Trade in? With 94334210056132972741600000 miles on the clock?
Do me a favour!

Smith yet! Most of them put 'Cohen'!

Would you believe 'The curtains don't go with the carpet'?
Such a terrible thing! And not a word about the stink!

So this is where you get your red nose!

Be reasonable — at least the conception was immaculate!

A lowly stable they said, but this lowly I didn't expect!

So what do you expect with a one star hotel?

You prefer the Miramar Beach Hotel? *Now* you tell me!

Not that we're complaining, but we were rather expecting Herald Angels!

The gold is nice! Frankincense and Myrhh he has plenty of!

Sing they don't — hum they most certainly do!

And also a life subscription to his trade journal!

RECIPE : BLINTZES.

"For the batter, you will need two eggs, ¼ pint of water, one ounce of melted marge, 2 oz. flour and a sprinkle of salt..

... for the filling – you will need 1 lb cottage cheese, 2 tablespoons sour cream, 2 eggs yolks, 3 tablespoons vanilla essence, ½ teaspoon salt and maybe raisins and maybe not.

. Then you mix all the filling ingredients together and spread it all over the blintzes. You can leave them flat, fold them, roll them up, make them into fan shapes... they're your blintzes.

..then you can brown them in butter or top them with sour cream whipped cream, berries, honey,. peanut butter, maple syrup, cavia or you can just leave them alone which is also good!

Mix the batter ingredients together and cook in a well greased pan till the batter sets...

.. then turn out, bottom side up into a cloth ... oops!

Try it—you'll like it!

Do me a favour!

All this excitement and you can *eat?*

He's the *image* of his father, am I right?

This is the part that always breaks me up!

We were praying for a boy, so I guess somewhere there's a God!

If you'd been there you could have had one!

I *myself* am also a Capricorn. God's children
us Capricorns!

A leather-bound Talmud with ivory inlay and
gold leaf is very nice Ruthie! But for *Christmas?*

It's plastic! Nice, huh?

J.C.? That's nice! We're AC/DC!

Again Beirut! Oy Gevald!

Would you take some advice from a Wise Man? Hold
the booze till they've gone, those shepherds!

All this and *still* you want an announcement in the Jewish Chronicle!

You want I should tell you something Ruthie? Your husband was some boy at the Christmas party!
So
So he's sixty three Ruthie, and chasing every pretty young shikse in sight!
Do dogs chase cars?
Yes?
And if a dog catches a car, can he drive it?

C'mon boss — its gone four and we've still got Africa to do!

Father *who?*

One day I want you should do your Momma a favour — Work a
miracle on your father!

It's my first time out — boy, what a schlep!

Yes, it's root beer. What did you expect in the Bible Belt? Scotch?

Two dinars for a Martini? Some rip-off!

"Tomorrow can you come back, Rabbi?"

"Every Christmas he gets like this, the chozzer!"

So if he's just an ordinary kid what's this — a bagel?

Already he's started!

And what do *I* get for Christmas? Zilch, that's what *I* get!

Of course the real joke is he's not even the father!

"Is it *my* fault you come at peak viewing time?"

"Not the father?" I said. "Then who is? An Angel?? You're putting me on!"

"They even sang one called 'Camel ye faithful'.
It was about *me,* I guess!"

This is positively the last Christmas I'm spending with your family!

Where have you *been* to get your Schmatteh in such a state?

I think he's going to be an intellectual!
Who in God's name can he take after?

He don't look much like a Messiah to me Becky!